I found this in the blogosphere...

A visit to a cinema is a little outing in itself.
It breaks the monotony of an afternoon or
evening; it gives a change from the
surroundings of home, however pleasant.

Ivor Novello

SOME THINGS ARE JUST FOR ME,...

A list of my favourite films:

_____

_____

_____

_____

_____

_____

_____

_____

_____

_____

_____

_____

_____

_____

_____

EVERY GREAT FILM SHOULD SEEM NEW EVERY TIME YOU SEE IT.

Roger Ebert

This took my breath away

Beauty often starts small and becomes immense.

Jean Cocteau

Things to do when I have some 'me' time

_____

_____

_____

_____

_____

_____

_____

_____

_____

_____

_____

IF I HAD KNOWN HOW OLD I WAS GOING TO BE
I'D HAVE TAKEN BETTER CARE OF MYSELF.

Adolph Zukor

IF IT'S NOT FUN, IT'S NOT WORTH DOING!

I joined a new Facebook group

_____

_____

_____

_____

_____

_____

_____

_____

_____

_____

_____

Hoping for a fabulous night out with friends

THE DARKNESS DECLARES THE GLORY OF LIGHT.
T S Elliot

Things to look forward to

A PHOTO TO REMIND ME OF A MAGICAL MOMENT

EVERYTHING THAT IRRITATES US ABOUT
OTHERS CAN LEAD US TO AN
UNDERSTANDING OF OURSELVES.

Carl Jung

WE MUST ACCEPT FINITE DISAPPOINTMENT, BUT NEVER LOSE INFINITE HOPE.

Martin Luther King, Jr.

I'm hoping for...

_____

_____

_____

_____

_____

_____

_____

_____

_____

_____

_____

_____

_____

_____

_____

_____

_____

I had to smile when I heard...

_____

_____

_____

_____

_____

_____

_____

_____

_____

_____

_____

_____

_____

_____

_____

I am proud of myself...

IT IS HARD, IF NOT IMPOSSIBLE, TO SNUB
A BEAUTIFUL WOMAN — THEY REMAIN
BEAUTIFUL AND THE SNUB RECOILS.

Winston Churchill

I want to tell the world about this great book I've just finished

_____

_____

_____

_____

_____

_____

_____

_____

_____

_____

_____

_____

TODAY NEARLY EVERYONE CAN READ, BUT ONLY

A FEW PEOPLE CAN THINK.

Cardinal Alfredo Ottaviani

I'm having a dinner party

_____

_____

_____

_____

_____

_____

_____

_____

WELL-BEHAVED WOMEN

RARELY MAKE HISTORY.

Laurel Ulrich

Try it, what have you got to lose!

_____

_____

_____

_____

_____

_____

_____

_____

_____

_____

_____

_____

_____

_____

Now this is a blog worth noting

OMG, I CAN'T BELIEVE SHE SAID THIS...

The possibilities are endless when the girls get together

_____

_____

_____

_____

_____

_____

_____

_____

_____

THERE ARE ONLY TWO KINDS OF WOMEN –

GODDESSES AND DOORMATS.

Pablo Picasso

WHEN ONE LOVES SOMEBODY EVERYTHING IS CLEAR — WHERE
TO GO, WHAT TO DO — IT ALL TAKES CARE OF ITSELF AND
ONE DOESN'T HAVE TO ASK ANYBODY ABOUT ANYTHING.

Maxim Gorky

At the cinema...

Must get to these gigs...

WE DO NOT SUCCEED IN CHANGING THINGS ACCORDING TO OUR DESIRE, BUT GRADUALLY OUR DESIRE CHANGES.

Marcel Proust

It's all on Twitter

_____

_____

_____

_____

_____

_____

_____

_____

_____

_____

_____

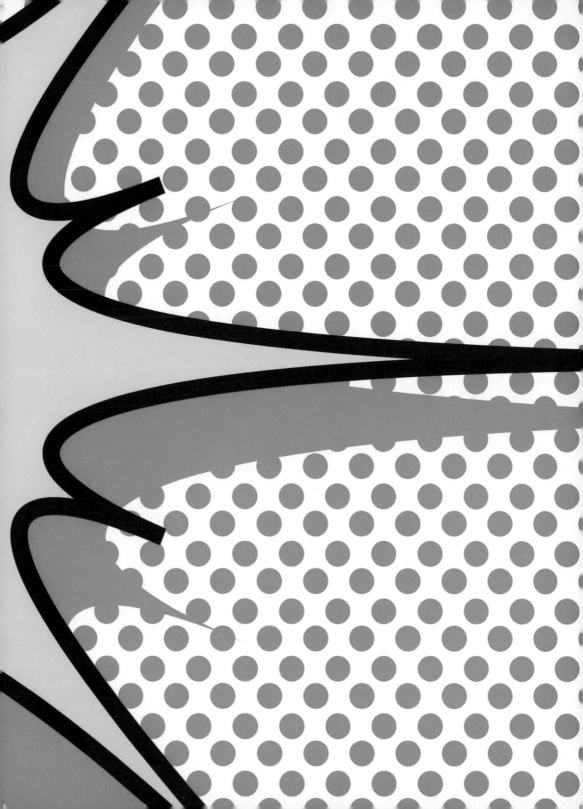

I MUST HAVE...

_____

_____

_____

_____

_____

_____

_____

_____

_____

_____

_____

_____

_____

_____

I'm loving this song...

_____

_____

_____

_____

_____

_____

_____

_____

_____

_____

... and want to play it over and over

MUSIC SHOULD BE YOUR ESCAPE.
Missy Elliot

These are my bad habits...

_____

_____

_____

_____

_____

_____

_____

_____

_____

_____

_____

_____

_____

_____

TO FALL INTO A HABIT IS TO BEGIN TO CEASE TO BE.

Miguel de Unamuno

... and I'm going to tame them!

I joined a new Facebook group

Make mine a...

A WOMAN SHOULD NEVER BE SEEN EATING OR DRINKING,
UNLESS IT BE LOBSTER SALAD AND CHAMPAGNE, THE ONLY
TRUE FEMININE AND BECOMING VIANDS.

Lord Byron

WHEN I'M GOOD I'M VERY GOOD,
BUT WHEN I'M BAD I'M BETTER.
Mae West

A great little restaurant has just opened

Steps to take to get to the top...

_____

_____

_____

_____

_____

_____

_____

_____

_____

_____

_____

_____

_____

_____

WOMEN NEVER HAVE YOUNG MINDS. THEY ARE BORN
THREE THOUSAND YEARS OLD.

Shelagh Delaney

A new cocktail recipe to share

_____

_____

_____

_____

_____

_____

_____

_____

_____

_____

_____

_____

_____

_____

_____

_____

A SPACE TO DRAW

ART WASHES AWAY FROM THE SOUL

THE DUST OF EVERYDAY LIFE.

Pablo Picasso

A SPACE TO THINK

_____

_____

_____

_____

_____

_____

_____

_____

_____

_____

_____

_____

_____

_____

_____

THINK OF ALL THE BEAUTY STILL LEFT
AROUND YOU AND BE HAPPY.

Anne Frank

ONE OF MY FAVOURITE PHOTOS

A MOODBOARD FOR ME... TODAY

HE WHO PASSIVELY ACCEPTS EVIL IS
AS MUCH INVOLVED IN IT AS HE WHO
HELPS PERPETRATE IT.

Martin Luther King, Jr.

This is something to Tweet about

I could dance all night to these songs...

_____

_____

_____

_____

_____

_____

_____

_____

_____

_____

_____

THE ONE THING THAT CAN SOLVE MOST OF OUR PROBLEMS IS DANCING.

James Brown

I SAW THIS, AND LAUGHED...

BETWEEN TWO EVILS I ALWAYS PICK THE
ONE I HAVE NEVER TRIED BEFORE.

Mae West

Dinner and drinks with my friends

_____

_____

_____

_____

_____

_____

_____

_____

_____

_____

_____

_____

_____

I'M REALLY LOOKING FORWARD TO...

A real page turner

_____

_____

_____

_____

_____

_____

_____

_____

_____

_____

_____

_____

_____

_____

IF ONE CANNOT ENJOY READING A BOOK OVER AND OVER
AGAIN, THERE IS NO USE IN READING IT AT ALL.

Oscar Wilde

I CAN'T MISS THIS...

I must have it!

_____

_____

_____

_____

_____

_____

_____

_____

_____

WITHOUT A SENSE OF URGENCY,

DESIRE LOSES ITS VALUE.

Jim Rohn

IN THE FRAME

I REALLY MUST...

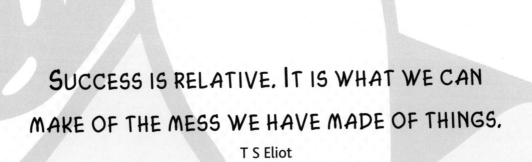

SUCCESS IS RELATIVE. IT IS WHAT WE CAN
MAKE OF THE MESS WE HAVE MADE OF THINGS.

T S Eliot

LAZINESS MAY APPEAR ATTRACTIVE, BUT WORK GIVES SATISFACTION.

Anne Frank

_____

_____

_____

_____

_____

_____

_____

_____

_____

_____

_____

_____

YOU HAVE GOT TO BE KIDDING!

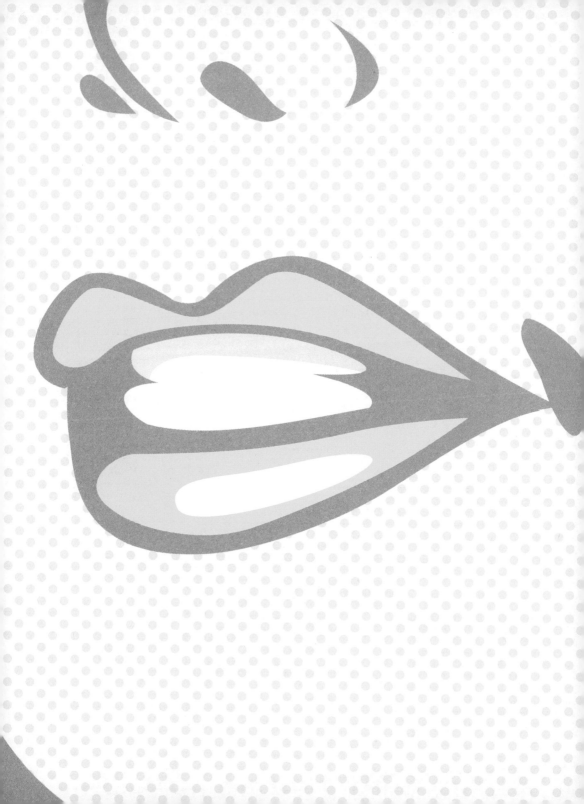

I laughed out loud

_____

_____

_____

_____

_____

_____

_____

_____

_____

_____

_____

LAUGHTER IS THE SUN THAT DRIVES

WINTER FROM THE HUMAN FACE.

Victor Hugo

I wish I'd written these books

SOME BOOKS ARE UNDESERVEDLY FORGOTTEN;
NONE ARE UNDESERVEDLY REMEMBERED.

W H Auden

GOODNESS IS EASIER TO RECOGNISE THAN TO DEFINE.

W H Auden

A new blog to keep me entertained

A kiss is still a kiss

IT IS THE TRUE NATURE OF MANKIND TO LEARN FROM MISTAKES, NOT FROM EXAMPLE.

Fred Hoyle

_____

_____

_____

_____

_____

_____

_____

_____

_____

_____

_____

_____

_____

WHAT ROCKS MY WORLD

_____

_____

_____

_____

_____

_____

_____

_____

_____

_____

_____

_____

_____

_____

_____

I'm watching...

_____

_____

_____

_____

_____

_____

_____

_____

_____

_____

_____

_____

_____

_____

_____

One is not born a woman,
One becomes one.

Simone de Beauvior

A PHOTO FROM LONG AGO

Success!

_____

_____

_____

_____

_____

_____

_____

_____

_____

_____

_____

MEET SUCCESS LIKE
A GENTLEMAN AND
DISASTER LIKE A MAN.

Lord Birkenhead

ONE DAY, I REALLY MUST...

_____

_____

_____

_____

_____

_____

_____

_____

_____

_____

_____

_____

_____

_____

Something amazing happened to me today

IT IS NO USE SPEAKING IN SOFT, GENTLE TONES
IF EVERYONE ELSE IS SHOUTING.

Joseph Priestley

It makes me mad when...

_____

_____

_____

_____

_____

_____

_____

_____

_____

_____

_____

_____

YOU CANNOT MAKE YOURSELF FEEL SOMETHING YOU
DO NOT FEEL, BUT YOU CAN MAKE YOURSELF DO RIGHT
IN SPITE OF YOUR FEELINGS.

Pearl S Buck

ON A DESERT ISLAND...

_____

_____

_____

_____

_____

_____

_____

_____

_____

_____

_____

_____

_____

_____

... THANK GOODNESS I HAVE THESE THINGS WITH ME

REMEMBER, REMEMBER...

Stuck indoors, what shall I do?

These songs put a bounce in my step

THIS KEEPS MY FEET ON THE GROUND

I would share my last bar of chocolate with...

_____

_____

_____

_____

_____

_____

_____

_____

_____

_____

_____

_____

_____

_____

SHARING FOOD WITH ANOTHER HUMAN BEING
IS AN INTIMATE ACT THAT SHOULD NOT BE
INDULGED IN LIGHTLY.

M F K Fisher

I'D LIKE TO GO ON BEING 35 FOR A LONG TIME.

Margaret Thatcher

A birthday party to plan

I'M REALLY LOOKING FORWARD TO...

_____

_____

_____

_____

_____

_____

_____

_____

_____

_____

_____

_____

_____

THE FEMALE OF THE SPECIES IS MORE DEADLY THAN THE MALE.

Rudyard Kipling

PARTING WORDS